# MAKING THE GRADE · GRADE 1

**EASY POPULAR PIECES FOR YOUNG VIOLINISTS. SELECTED AND ARRANGED BY JERRY LANNING. EDITED BY MARJORY KING**

Exclusive Distributors:
Music Sales Limited
Newmarket Road, Bury St. Edmunds, Suffolk IP33 3YB.
This book © Copyright 1995 Chester Music.
ISBN 0-7119-5053-9
Order No. CH61085
Cover design and typesetting by Pemberton and Whitefoord.
Music engraved by Seton Music Graphics Ltd.
Printed in the United Kingdom by
Caligraving Limited, Thetford, Norfolk.

## Chester Music

(A division of Music Sales Limited)
8/9 Frith Street, London W1V 5TZ

1

# INTRODUCTION

This collection of 21 popular tunes has been carefully arranged and graded to provide attractive teaching repertoire for young violinists. The familiarity of the material will stimulate pupils' enthusiasm and encourage their practice.

The technical demands of the solo part increase progressively up to the standard of Associated Board Grade 1. The piano accompaniments are simple yet effective and should be within the range of most pianists.

Practical suggestions for fingering are given, but these may of course be adapted to suit the needs of the individual student. It is important always to feel a steady pulse, so that bow speeds can be planned appropriately.

# CONTENTS

# LOVE ME TENDER

*Words & Music by Elvis Presley & Vera Matson.*

Play the phrases smoothly, and keep a steady tempo.
Try to use plenty of bow to make the music sing.

**Moderately**

# WE ALL STAND TOGETHER

*Words & Music by Paul McCartney.*

Take care to feel the three beats in your bow.

**Quite brightly**

# BANKS OF THE OHIO

*Traditional.*

Start in the middle of the bow, and save your bow on the longer notes.

**Gently**

# ON CHRISTMAS NIGHT

*Traditional.*

Try to keep this carol moving, with only one accent in a bar.

**Flowing**

# ODE TO JOY (THEME FROM THE 9TH SYMPHONY)

*Composed by Ludwig Van Beethoven.*

This is the main theme from one of Beethoven's biggest works.
It needs a good, strong sound, so use plenty of bow.

# SOMETIMES WHEN WE TOUCH

*Words & Music by Dan Hill & Barry Mann.*

Although there are a number of repeated notes here,
this piece should generally sound smooth and sustained.

# BLOWIN' IN THE WIND

*Words & Music by Bob Dylan.*

Notice how the first four-bar phrase is repeated five times with slight variations,
and 'answered' by the final eight bars.

**Flowing**

# TALES OF THE UNEXPECTED (THEME FROM)

*Composed by Ron Grainer.*

This is the theme from the popular TV series.

Notice the clever mixture of three-, four- and five-bar phrases which give it a haunting quality

# I'D LIKE TO TEACH THE WORLD TO SING

*Words & Music by Roger Cook, Roger Greenaway, Billy Backer & Billy Davis.*

Use your fourth finger to stay on the same string and help maintain tone colour.

# UNCHAINED MELODY

*Music by Alex North. Words by Hy Zaret.*

Notice the time signature and think in minims rather than crotchets.

**Moderately slow**

# MORNING HAS BROKEN

*Music Traditional.*

Practise the scale and arpeggio of D major before you tackle this one.

Notice the different rhythms in bars 13 and 25, and use the whole bow for each bar.

**Gently moving**

# JINGLE BELLS

*Traditional.*

Start your bow at the point and stop it in the middle for the double up bow.

# FIDDLER ON THE ROOF

Music by Jerry Bock. Lyrics by Sheldon Harnick.

Try playing this piece sometimes *legato*, and sometimes with a more lifted bow stroke for contrast.

# LITTLE BROWN JUG

*Traditional.*

Make sure all the quavers are really even.
You will need very little bow for the semiquavers.

**Quite lively**

# SCARBOROUGH FAIR

*Traditional.*

Take care to bow very gently, especially on the open strings.

**Moderately**

# AMAZING GRACE

*Traditional.*

The up bows need to be faster and lighter than the down bows to maintain an even sound.

# ONE DAY AT A TIME

*Words & Music by Willie Nelson.*

This beautiful gospel song was a big hit a few years back.

Make sure you hold the tied notes for their full value by slowing down your bow.

# THIS OLE HOUSE

*Words & Music by Stuart Hamblen.*

Here's a lively American country and western song which will give you practice in repeated notes.
Accent the first beat in each bar slightly. You will find it most comfortable to play in the middle of the bow.

**Brightly**

# HEY JUDE (1ST VERSION)

*Words & Music by John Lennon & Paul McCartney.*

If you find the rhythms in this Beatles song tricky, try the version opposite first,
where the note lengths have been doubled.

**Quite slowly (in 4)**

# HEY JUDE (2ND VERSION)

*Words & Music by John Lennon & Paul McCartney.*

If you count four in a bar to begin with, you'll have no trouble with the rhythms.
When you are able to play up to speed (counting in two), go back to the first version.

**Quite slowly (in 2)**

# COUNTRY GARDENS

*Traditional.*

In general use the upper half of your bow,
but suddenly less bow in bars 12 and 20, which echo the preceding bars.

**Quite brightly**

# EASTENDERS

*Composed by Leslie Osborne & Simon May.*

Be careful not to rush the triplet crotchets, but give them a broad, slightly lazy feel.

9/97 (28802)